DOT to DOT

COLORING BOOK

Round Duck

Vol.1

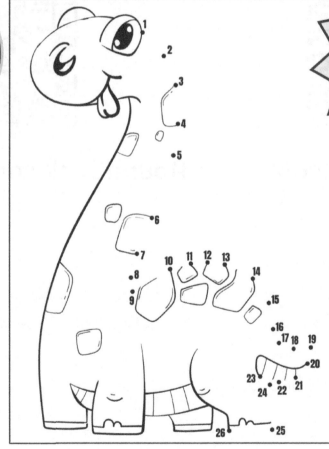

FOR KIDS AGES 4-8

Visit our Website to Check Out All of Our Fun Activity and Puzzle Books for Children of All Ages

Subscribe to Our Newsletter to Keep Up to Date with Our New Releases, Freebies, and Everything Round Duck

RoundDuck.com

RoundDuck.com/Subscribe

THIS BOOK BELONGS TO:

_____

This page is intentionally left blank to stop your colors from seeping through to the next page

KEEPING BOOKS IN THE HANDS OF YOUNG MINDS

WORD SEARCH
FOR KIDS AGES 4-6
Vol.1

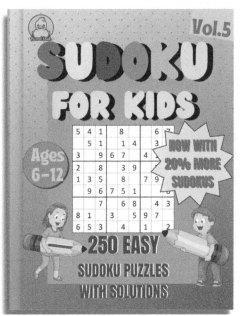

Vol.5
SUDOKU
FOR KIDS
Ages 6-12
NOW WITH 20% MORE SUDOKUS
250 EASY
SUDOKU PUZZLES
WITH SOLUTIONS

LETTER TRACING
HANDWRITING PRACTICE
Trace Letter - A
Vol.1
A is for Apple
FOR KIDS AGES 4-6

MANDALA
COLORING BOOK
Vol.1
FOR KIDS AGES 4-6

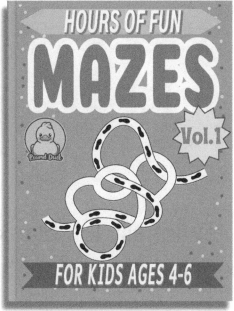

HOURS OF FUN
MAZES
Vol.1
FOR KIDS AGES 4-6

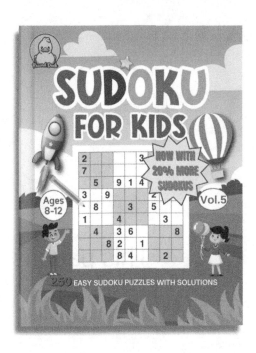

SUDOKU
FOR KIDS
NOW WITH 20% MORE SUDOKUS
Ages 8-12
Vol.5
250 EASY SUDOKU PUZZLES WITH SOLUTIONS

This page is intentionally left blank to stop your colors from seeping through to the next page

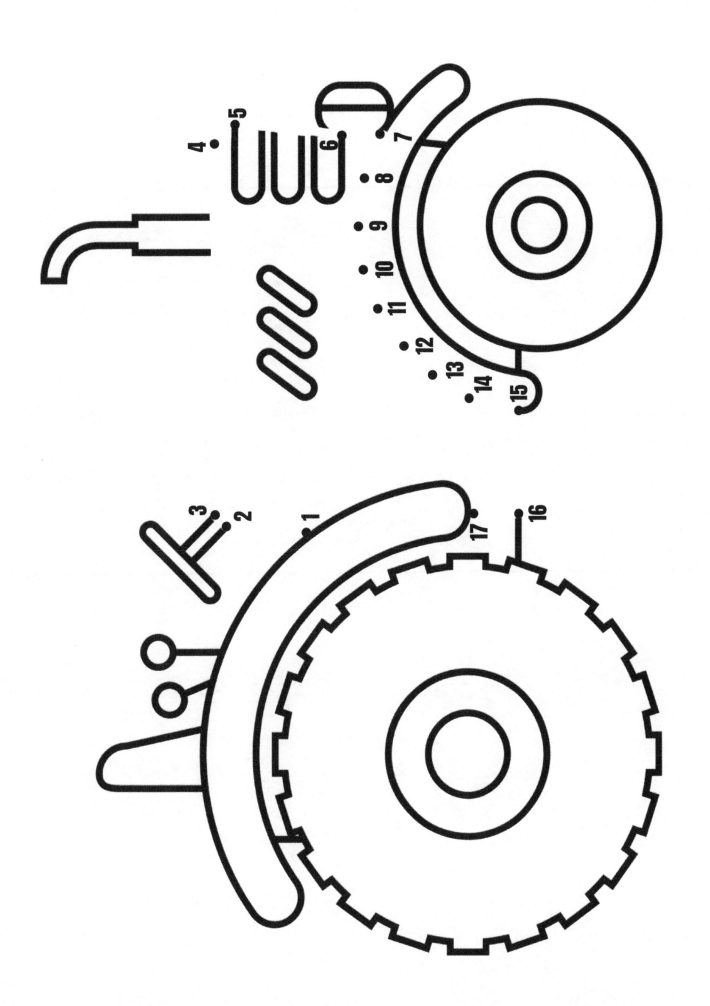

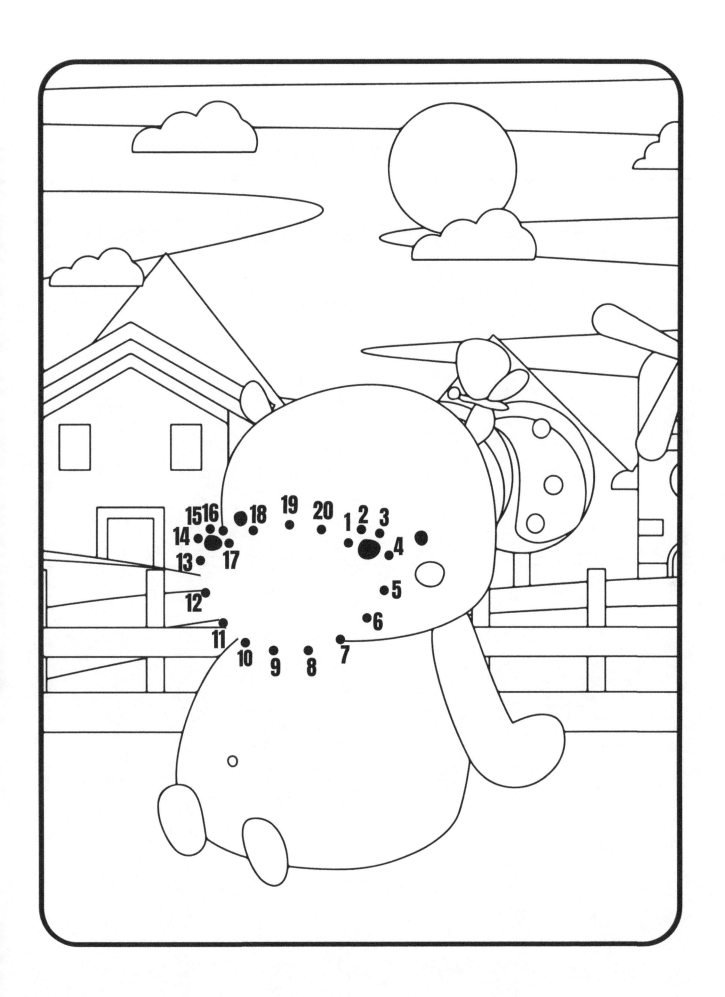

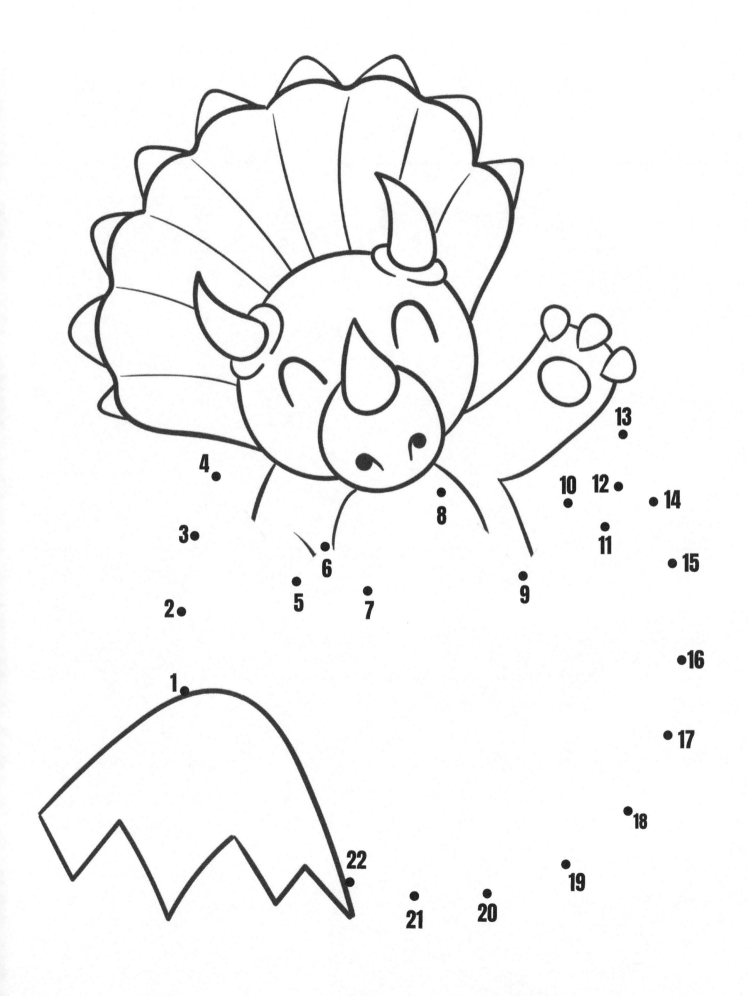

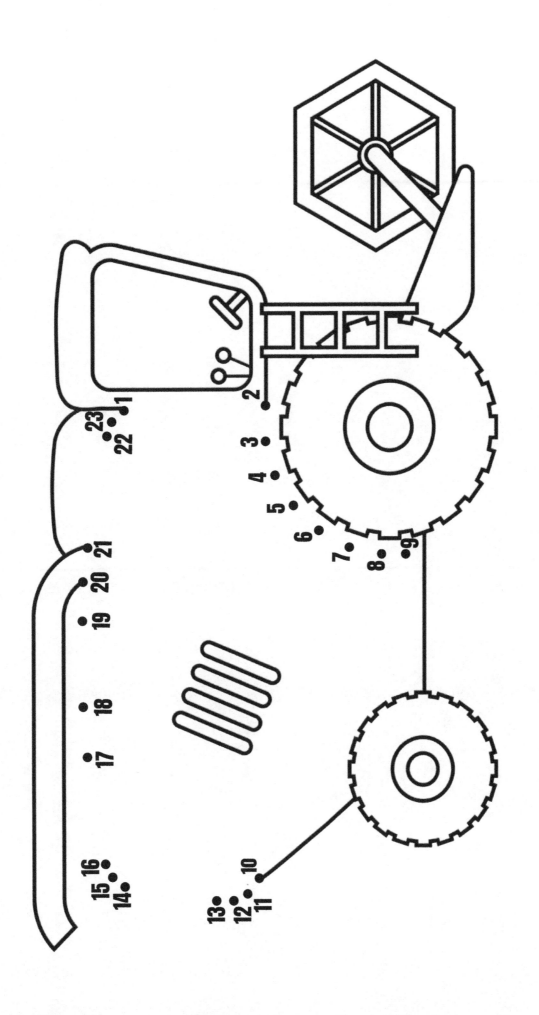

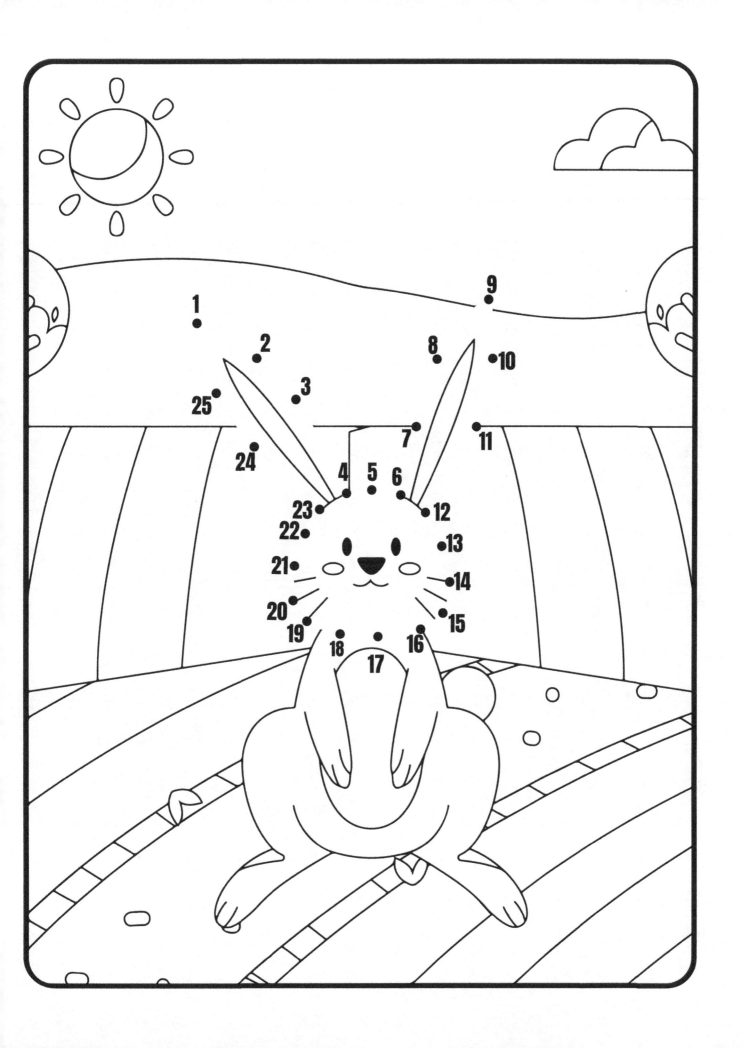

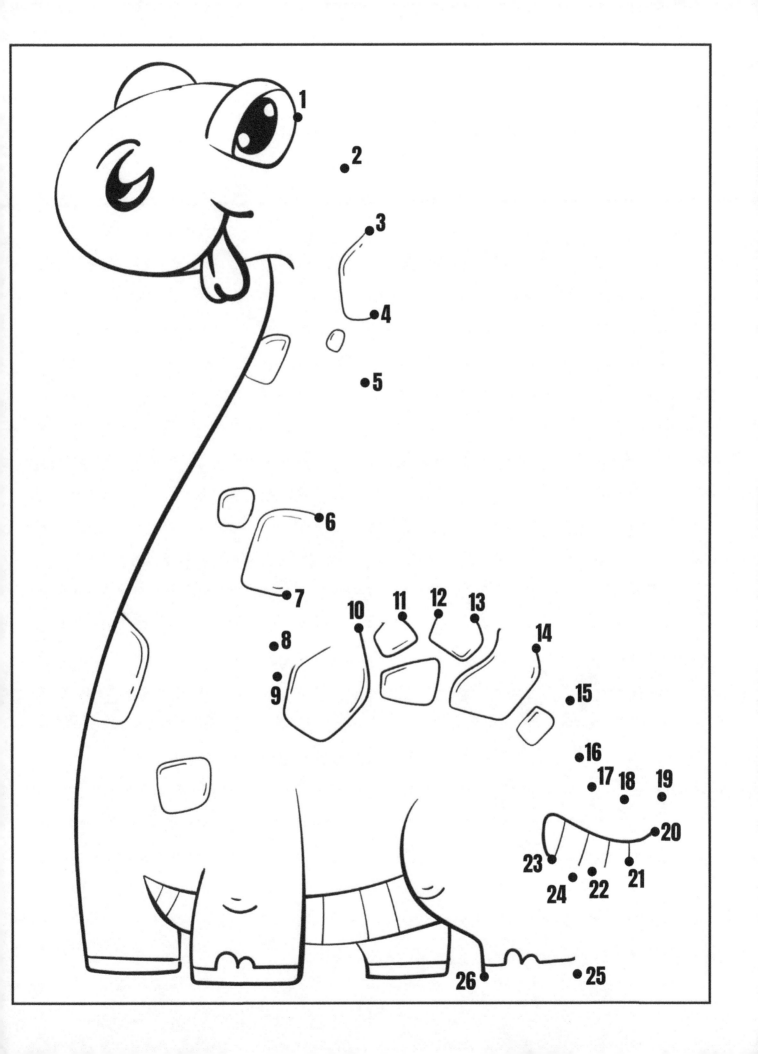

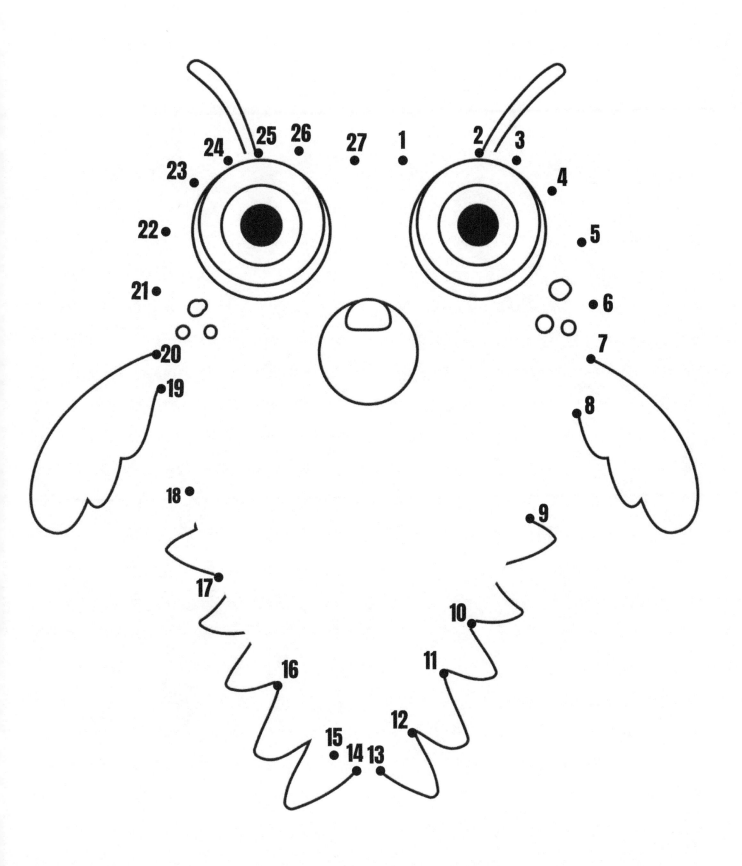

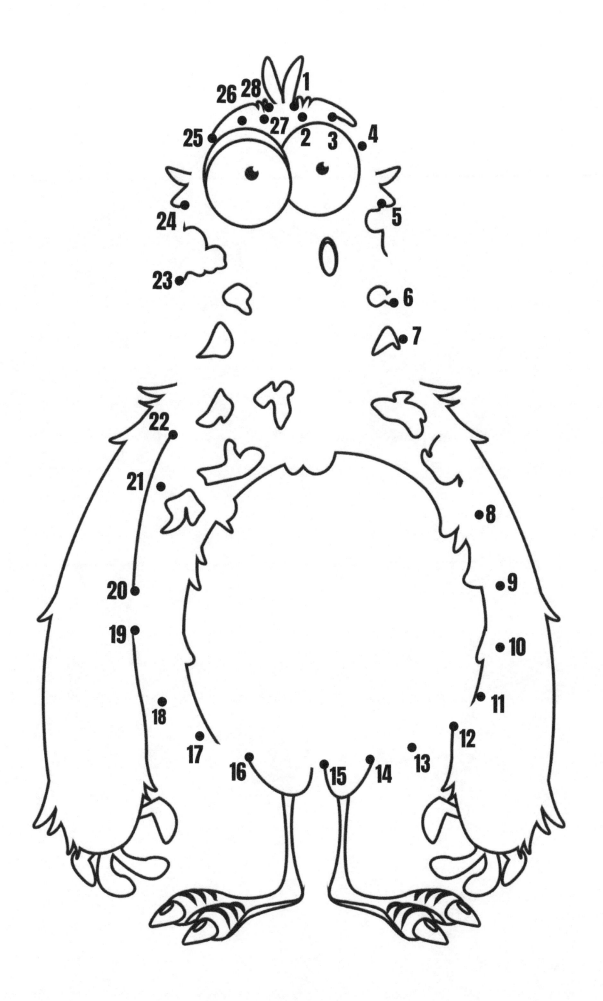

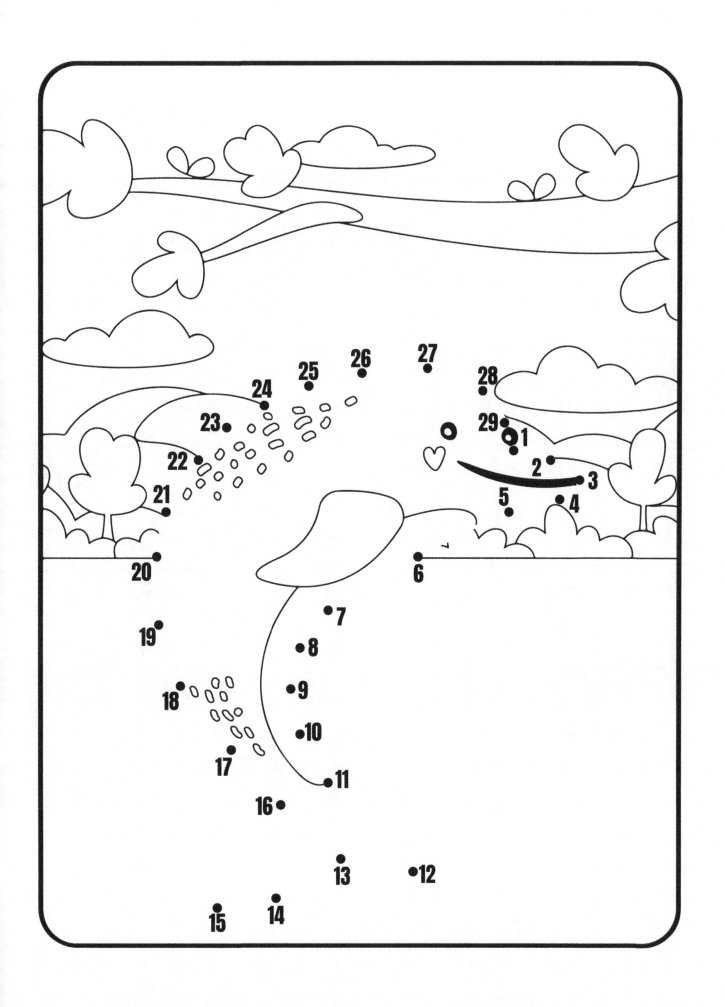

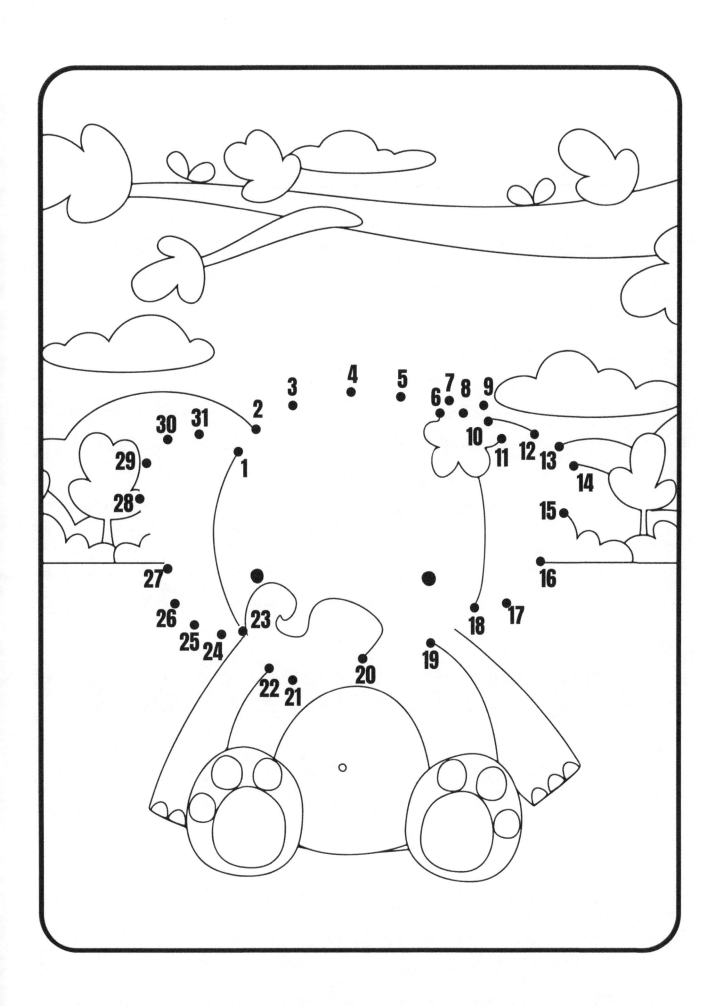

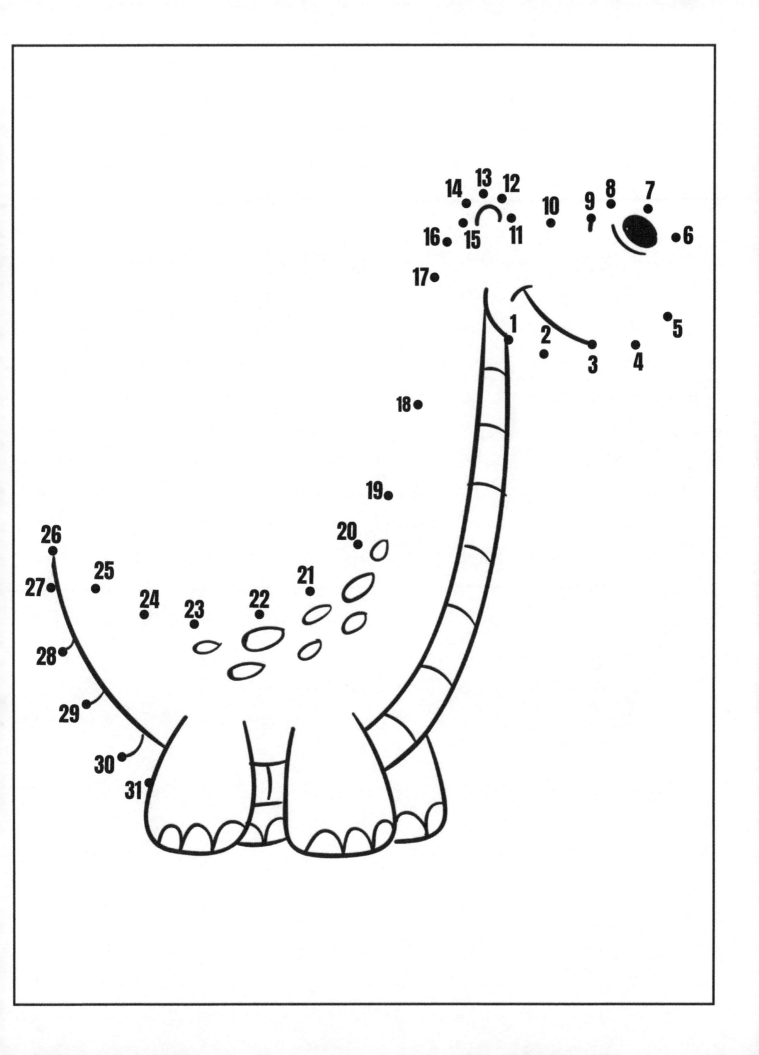

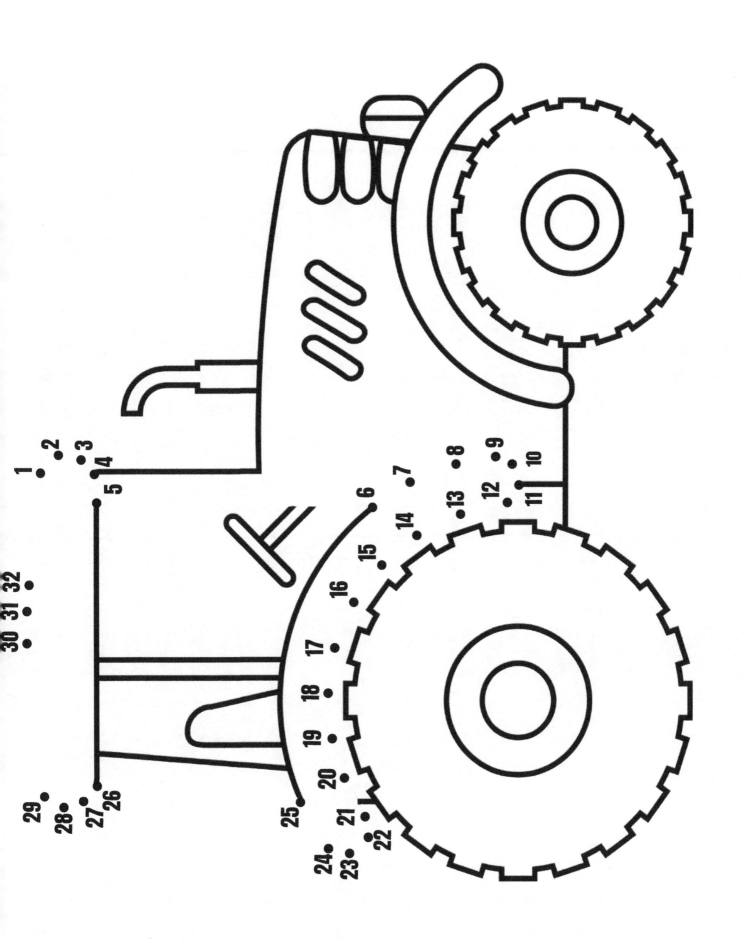

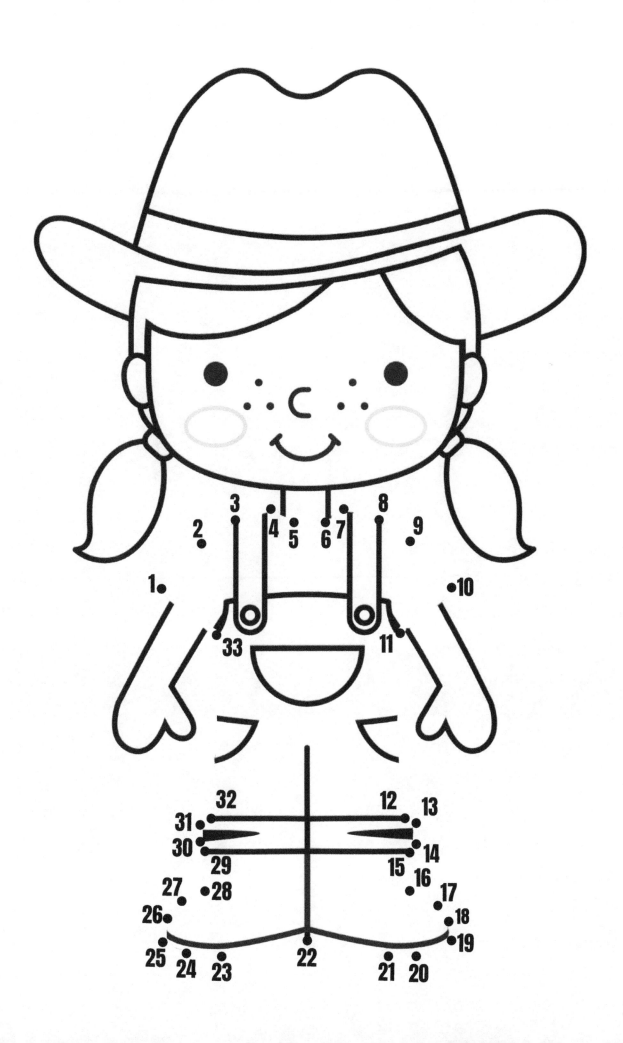

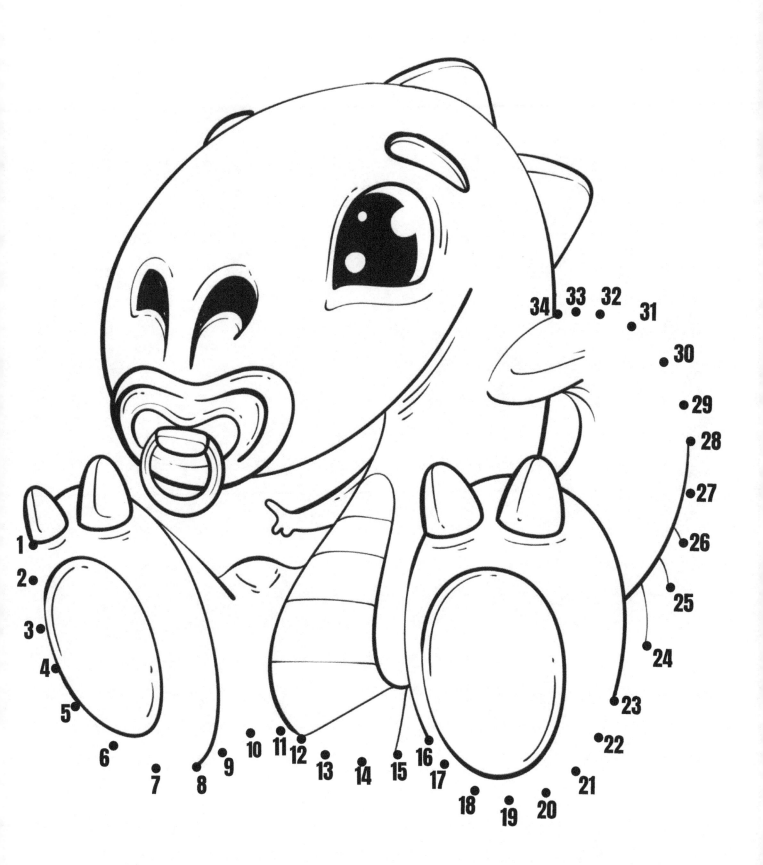

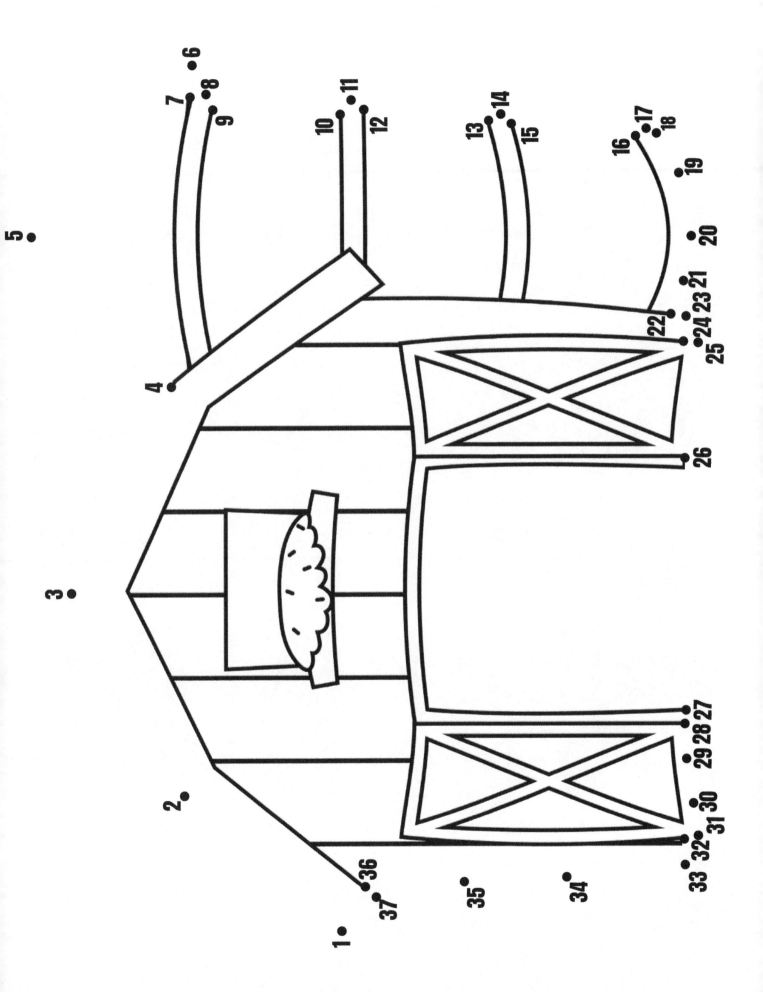

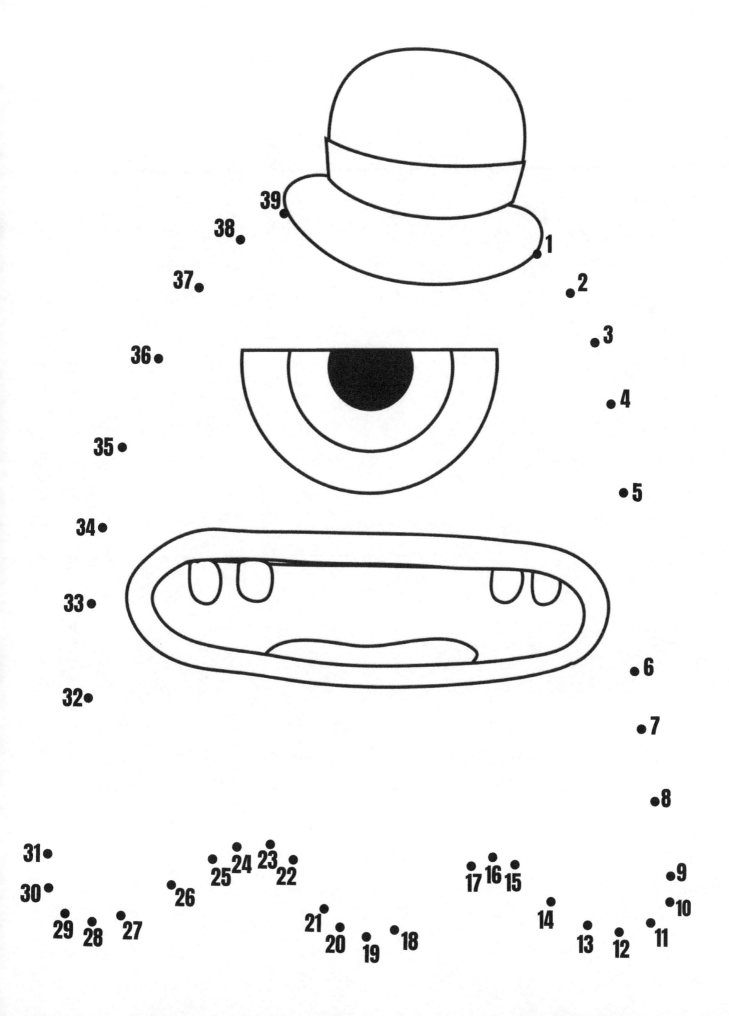

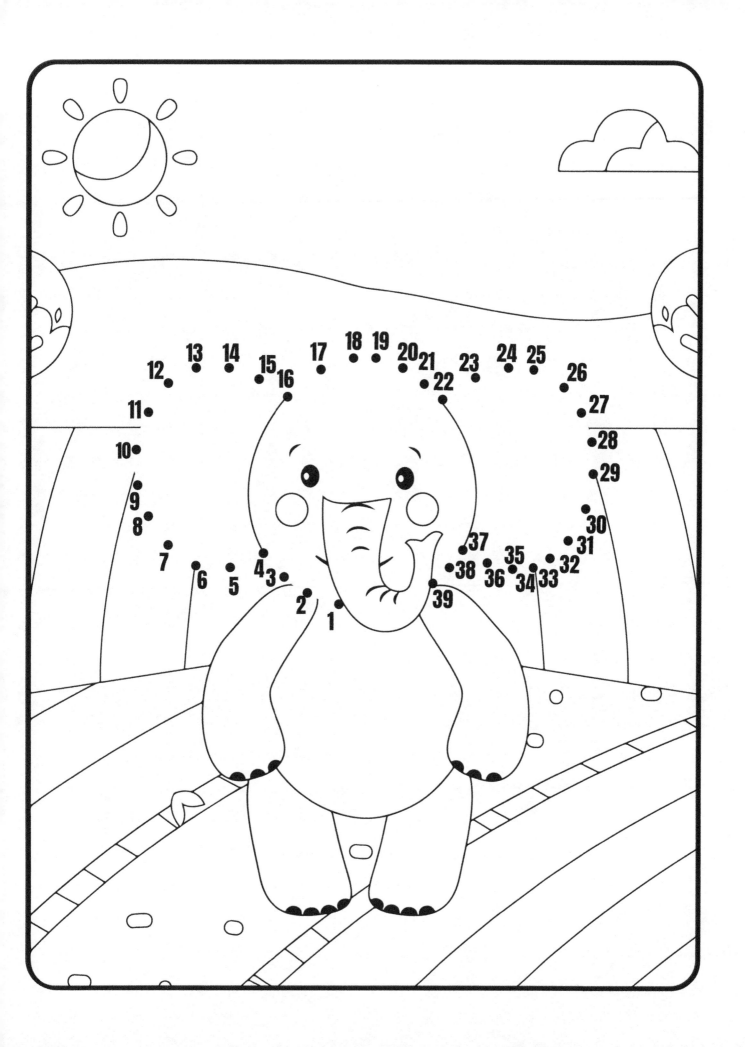

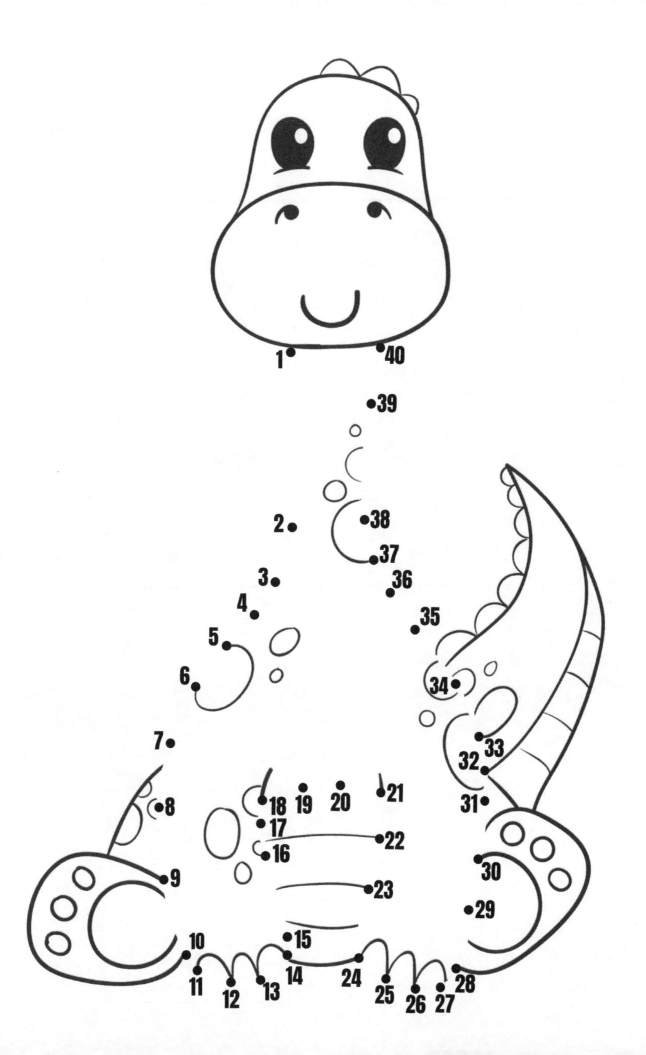